*Every Species is a
Masterpiece*

Every Species is a Masterpiece

EDWARD O. WILSON

PENGUIN BOOKS — GREEN IDEAS

PENGUIN BOOKS

UK | USA | Canada | Ireland | Australia
India | New Zealand | South Africa

Penguin Books is part of the Penguin Random House group of companies
whose addresses can be found at global.penguinrandomhouse.com.

'Is Humanity Suicidal?' (First published in *The Sunday New York Times Magazine*,
30 May 1993, pp. 24–29). From *In Search of Nature* by Edward O. Wilson. Copyright
© 1996 Island Press. Reproduced by permission of Island Press, Washington, DC.
'The Environmental Ethic' (First published in *Hastings Environmental
Law Journal*, 3(2), pp. 327–331 (1996)). From *The Diversity of Life* by
Edward O. Wilson. Copyright © 1994 Penguin Books
'Biophilia and the Environmental Ethic' (First published as 'Biophilia and the
Conservation Ethic' in S. Kellert and E. O. Wilson *The Biophilia Hypothesis*,
pp. 31–41 (1993)). From *In Search of Nature* by Edward O. Wilson. Copyright © 1996
Island Press. Reproduced by permission of Island Press, Washington, DC.
'Vanishing Before Our Eyes' (First published in *Time Magazine*, 26 April 2000).
'Half-Earth' from *Half-Earth: Our Planet's Fight for Life* by Edward O. Wilson.
Copyright © Edward O. Wilson, 2016. Used by permission of
Liveright Publishing Corporation.
This selection first published in Penguin Books 2021

001

Copyright © Edward O. Wilson, 1993, 1996, 2000

Set in 12.5/15pt Dante MT Std
Typeset by Jouve (UK), Milton Keynes
Printed and bound in Great Britain by Clays Ltd, Elcograf S.p.A.

The authorized representative in the EEA is Penguin Random House Ireland,
Morrison Chambers, 32 Nassau Street, Dublin D02 YH68

A CIP catalogue record for this book is available from the British Library

ISBN: 978–0–241–51455–9

www.greenpenguin.co.uk

Contents

Is Humanity Suicidal?

Imagine that on an icy moon of Jupiter – say, Ganymede – the space station of an alien civilization is concealed. For millions of years its scientists have closely watched Earth. Because their law prevents settlement on a living planet, they have tracked the surface by means of satellites equipped with sophisticated sensors, mapping the spread of large assemblages of organisms, from forests, grasslands, and tundras to coral reefs and the vast planktonic meadows of the sea. They have recorded millennial cycles in the climate, interrupted by the advance and retreat of glaciers and scatter-shot volcanic eruptions.

The watchers have been waiting for what might be called the Moment. When it comes, occupying only a few centuries and thus a mere tick in geological time, the forests shrink back to less than half their original cover. Atmospheric carbon dioxide rises to the highest level in 100,000 years. The ozone layer of the stratosphere thins, and holes open at the poles. Plumes of nitrous oxide and other toxins rise from fires in South America and Africa, settle in the upper troposphere, and drift eastward across the oceans. At night the land surface brightens with millions of pinpoints of light, which coalesce into blazing swaths across Europe, Japan, and eastern North America. A semicircle of fire spreads from gas flares around the Persian Gulf.

It was all but inevitable, the watchers might tell us if we met them, that from the great diversity of large animals, one species or another would eventually gain intelligent control of Earth. That role has fallen to *Homo sapiens*, a primate risen in Africa from a lineage that split away from the chimpanzee line 5 to 8 million years ago. Unlike any creature that lived before, we have become a geophysical force, swiftly changing the atmosphere and climate as well as the composition of the world's fauna and flora. Now in the midst of a population explosion, the human species has doubled to 5.5 billion during the past 50 years. It is scheduled to double again in the next 50 years. No other single species in evolutionary history has even remotely approached the sheer mass in protoplasm generated by humanity.

Darwin's dice have rolled badly for Earth. It was a misfortune for the living world in particular, many scientists believe, that a carnivorous primate and not some more benign form of animal made the breakthrough. Our species retains hereditary traits that add greatly to our destructive impact. We are tribal and aggressively territorial, intent on private space beyond minimal requirements, and oriented by selfish sexual and reproductive drives. Cooperation beyond the family and tribal levels comes hard.

Worse, our liking for meat causes us to use the sun's energy at low efficiency. It is a general rule of ecology that (very roughly) only about 10 percent of the sun's energy captured by photosynthesis to produce plant tissue is converted

3

into energy in the tissue of herbivores, the animals that eat the plants. Of that amount, 10 percent reaches the tissue of the carnivores feeding on the herbivores. Similarly, only 10 percent is transferred to carnivores. And so on for another step or two. In a wetlands chain that runs from marsh grass to grasshopper to warbler to hawk, the energy captured during green production shrinks a thousandfold.

In other words, it takes a great deal of grass to support a hawk. Human beings, like hawks, are top carnivores, at the end of the food chain whenever they eat meat, two or more links removed from the plants; if chicken, for example, two links; and if tuna, four links. Even with most societies confined today to a largely vegetarian diet, humanity is gobbling up a large part of the rest of the living world. We appropriate between 20 and 40 percent of the sun's energy that would otherwise be fixed into the tissue of natural vegetation, principally by our consumption of crops and timber, construction of buildings and roadways, and creation of wastelands. In the relentless search for more food we have reduced animal life in lakes, rivers, and now, increasingly, the open ocean. And everywhere we pollute the air and water, lower water tables, and extinguish species.

The human species is, in a word, an environmental hazard. It is possible that intelligence in the wrong kind of species was foreordained to be a fatal combination for the biosphere. Perhaps a law of evolution is that intelligence usually extinguishes itself.

This admittedly dour scenario is based on what can be termed the juggernaut theory of human nature, which holds that people are programmed by their genetic heritage to be so selfish that a sense of global responsibility will come too late. Individuals place themselves first, family second, tribe third, and the rest of the world a distant fourth. Their genes also predispose them to plan ahead for at most one or two generations. They fret over the petty problems and conflicts of their daily lives and respond swiftly and often ferociously to slight challenges to their status and tribal security. But oddly, as psychologists have discovered, humans also tend to underestimate both the likelihood and impact of such natural disasters as major earthquakes and great storms.

The reason for this myopic fog, evolutionary biologists contend, is that it was actually advantageous during all but the last few millennia of the 2 million years of existence of the genus *Homo.* The brain evolved into its present form during this long stretch of evolutionary time, during which humans existed in small, preliterate hunter-gatherer bands. Life was precarious and short. A premium was placed on close attention to the near future and early reproduction, and little else. Disasters of a magnitude that occurred only once every few centuries were forgotten or transmuted into myth. So today the human mind still works comfortably backward and forward for only a few years, spanning a period not exceeding one or two generations. Those in past ages whose genes inclined them to short-term thinking lived longer and had more children than those who did not. Prophets never enjoyed a Darwinian edge.

The rules have recently changed, however. Global crises are proliferating within the life span of the generation now coming of age, a foreshortening that may explain why young people express more concern about the environment than do their elders. The time scale has contracted because of the exponential growth in both the human population and technologies impacting the environment. Exponential growth is basically the same as the increase of wealth by compound interest. The larger the population, the faster the growth; the faster the growth, the sooner the population becomes still larger. In Nigeria, to cite one of our more fecund nations, the population is expected to double from its 1988 level to 216 million by the year 2010. If the same rate of growth were to continue to 2110, Nigeria's population would exceed that of the entire present population of the world.

With people everywhere seeking a better quality of life, the search for resources is expanding even faster than the population. The demand is being met by an increase in scientific knowledge, which doubles every 10 to 15 years.

It is accelerated further by a parallel rise in environment-devouring technology. Because Earth is finite in many resources that determine the quality of life – including arable soil, nutrients, fresh water, and space for natural ecosystems – doubling of consumption at constant intervals can bring disaster with shocking suddenness. Even when a nonrenewable resource has been only half used, it is still only one interval away from the end. Ecologists like to make this point with the French riddle of the lily pond. At first there is only one lily pad in the pond, but the next day it doubles, and thereafter each of its descendants doubles. The pond completely fills with lily pads in 30 days. When is the pond exactly half full? Answer: on the twenty-ninth day.

Yet, mathematical exercises aside, who can safely measure the human capacity to overcome the perceived limits of Earth? The question of central interest is this: Are we racing to the brink of an abyss, or are we just gathering speed for a takeoff to a wonderful future? The crystal ball is clouded; the human condition baffles all the more because it is both unprecedented and bizarre, almost beyond understanding.

In the midst of uncertainty, opinions on the human prospect have tended to fall loosely into two schools. The first, exemptionalism, holds that since humankind is transcendent in intelligence and spirit, our species must have been released from the iron laws of ecology that bind all other species. However serious the problem, civilized human beings, by ingenuity, force of will, and – who knows – divine dispensation, will find a solution.

Population growth? Good for the economy, claim some of the exemptionalists, and in any case a basic human right, so let it run. Land shortages? Try fusion energy to power the desalting of seawater, then reclaim the world's deserts. (The process might be assisted by towing icebergs to coastal pipelines.) Species going extinct? Not to worry. That is nature's way. Think of humankind as only the latest in a long line of exterminating agents in geological time. In any case, because our species has pulled free of old-style, mindless Nature, we have begun a different order of life. Evolution should now be allowed to proceed along this new trajectory. Finally, resources? The planet has more than enough resources to last indefinitely, if human genius is allowed to address each new problem in turn, without alarmist and unreasonable restrictions imposed on economic development. So hold the course, and touch the brakes lightly.

The opposing idea of reality is environmentalism, which sees humanity as a biological species tightly dependent on the natural world. However formidable our intellect may be and however fierce our spirit, the argument goes, those qualities are not enough to free us from the constraints of the natural environment in which the human ancestors evolved. We cannot draw confidence from successful solutions to the smaller problems of the past. Many of Earth's vital resources are about to be exhausted, its atmospheric chemistry is deteriorating, and human populations have already grown dangerously large. Natural ecosystems, the wellsprings of a healthful environment, are being irreversibly degraded.

At the heart of the environmentalist world-view is the conviction that human physical and spiritual health depends on sustaining the planet in a relatively unaltered state. Earth is our home in the full, genetic sense, where humanity and its ancestors existed for all the millions of years of their evolution. Natural ecosystems – forests, coral reefs, marine blue waters – maintain the world exactly as we would wish it to be maintained. When we debase the global environment and extinguish the variety of life, we are dismantling a support system that is too complex to understand, let alone replace, in the foreseeable future. Space scientists theorize the existence of a virtually unlimited array of other planetary environments, almost all of which are uncongenial to human life. Our own Mother Earth, lately called Gaia, is a specialized conglomerate of organisms and the physical environment they create on a day-to-day basis, which can be destabilized and turned lethal by careless activity. We run the risk, conclude the environmentalists, of beaching ourselves upon alien shores like a great confused pod of pilot whales.

If my tone here has not already made my own position clear, I now explicitly place myself in the environmentalist school. I am not so radical as to wish for a turning back of the clock; I am not given to driving spikes into Douglas firs to prevent logging; and I am distinctly uneasy with such hybrid movements as ecofeminism, which holds that Mother Earth is a nurturing home for all life and should be revered and loved as in premodern (paleolithic and archaic) societies and that ecosystem abuse is rooted in androcentric – that is, male-dominated – concepts, values, and institutions. Still, product of androcentric culture though I am, I am radical enough to take seriously the question heard with increasing frequency: Is humanity suicidal? Is the drive to environmental conquest and self-propagation embedded so deeply in our genes as to be unstoppable?

My short answer – opinion, if you wish – is that humanity is not suicidal, at least not in the sense just stated. We are smart enough and have time enough to avoid an environmental catastrophe of civilization-threatening dimensions.

But the technical problems are sufficiently formidable to require a redirection of much of science and technology, and the ethical issues are so basic as to force a reconsideration of our self-image as a species.

There are reasons for optimism, reasons to believe that we have entered what might someday be generously called the Century of the Environment. The United Nations Conference on Environment and Development, held in Rio de Janeiro in June 1992, attracted more than 120 heads of government, the largest number ever assembled, and helped move environmental issues closer to the political center stage; on November 18, 1992, more than 1,500 senior scientists from 69 countries issued a 'Warning to Humanity,' stating that overpopulation and environmental deterioration have put the very future of life at risk. The greening of religion has become a global trend, with theologians and religious leaders addressing environmental problems as a moral issue. In May 1992, leaders of most of the major American denominations met with scientists as guests of the U.S. Senate to formulate a 'Joint Appeal by Religion and Science for the Environment.' Conservation of biodiversity is increasingly seen by national governments and major landowners alike as important to their country's future. Indonesia, home to a large share of the native Asian plant and animal species, has begun to shift to land-management practices that conserve and sustainably develop the remaining rain forests. Costa Rica has created a National Institute of Biodiversity. A Pan-African institute for biodiversity research and management has been founded, with headquarters in Zimbabwe.

Finally, there are favorable demographic signs. The rate of population increase is declining on all continents, although it is still well above zero almost everywhere and remains especially high in sub-Saharan Africa. Despite entrenched traditions and religious beliefs, the desire to use contraceptives in family planning is spreading. Demographers estimate that if the demand were fully met, contraceptive use alone would reduce the eventual stabilized population by more than 2 billion.

In summary, the will is there. Yet the awful truth remains that a large part of humanity will suffer no matter what is done. The number of people living in absolute poverty has risen during the past 20 years to nearly one billion and is expected to increase another 100 million by the end of the decade. Whatever progress has been made in the developing countries, and that includes an overall improvement in the average standard of living, is threatened by a continuance of rapid population growth and the deterioration of forests and arable soil.

Our hopes must be chastened further still, and this is the central issue, by a key and seldom-recognized distinction between the nonliving and living environments. Science and the political process can be adapted to manage the nonliving physical environment. The human hand is now upon the physical homeostat. The ozone layer can be mostly restored to the upper atmosphere by elimination of CFCs, with these substances peaking at six times the present level and then subsiding during the next half-century. Also, with procedures that will prove far more difficult and initially expensive, carbon dioxide and other greenhouse gases can be pulled back to concentrations that slow global warming.

The human hand, however, is *not* upon the biological homeostat. There is no way in sight to micromanage the natural ecosystems and the millions of species they contain. That feat might be accomplished by generations to come, but then it will be too late for the ecosystems – and perhaps for us. Despite the seemingly fathomless extent of creation, humankind has been chipping away at its diversity, and Earth is destined to become an impoverished planet within a century if present trends continue. Mass extinctions are being reported with increasing frequency in every part of the world. They include half the freshwater fishes of peninsular Malaysia, half the 41 tree snails of Oahu, 44 of the 68 shallow-water mussels of the Tennessee River shoals, as many as 90 plant species growing on the Centinela Ridge in Ecuador, and, in the United States as a whole, about 200 plant species, with another 680 species and races now classified as in danger of extinction. The main cause is the destruction of natural habitats, especially tropical forests. Close behind, especially on the Hawaiian archipelago and other islands, is the introduction of rats, pigs, beard grass, lantana, and other exotic organisms that outbreed and extirpate native species.

The few thousand biologists worldwide who specialize in diversity are aware that they can witness and report no more than a very small percentage of the extinctions actually occurring. The reason is that they have facilities to keep track of only a tiny fraction of the millions of species and a sliver of the planet's surface on a yearly basis. They have devised a general standard by which to characterize the situation: that whenever careful studies are made of habitats before and after disturbance, extinctions almost always come to light. The corollary: the great majority of extinctions are never observed. Vast numbers of species are apparently vanishing before they can be discovered and named.

There is a way, nonetheless, to estimate the rate of loss indirectly. Independent studies around the world and in fresh and marine waters have revealed a robust connection between the size of a habitat and the amount of biodiversity it contains. Even a small loss in area reduces the number of species. The relation is such that when the area of the habitat is cut to one-tenth of its original cover, the number of species eventually drops by roughly one-half. Tropical rain forests, thought to harbor a majority of Earth's species (the reason conservationists get so exercised about rain forests), are being reduced by nearly that magnitude. At the present time they occupy about the same total area as that of the forty-eight conterminous United States, representing a little less than half their original, prehistoric cover; and they are shrinking each year by well over 1 percent, an amount equal to half the state of Florida. If the typical value (that is, 90 percent area loss causes 50 percent eventual extinction) is applied, the projected loss of species due to rain forest destruction worldwide is 0.3 percent across the board for all kinds of plants, animals, and microorganisms.

When area reduction and all the other extinction agents are considered together, it is reasonable to project a reduction by 20 percent or more of the rain forest species by the year 2020, climbing to 50 percent or more by midcentury, if nothing is done to change current practice. Comparable erosion is likely in other environments now under assault, including many coral reefs and Mediterranean-type heathlands of Western Australia, South Africa, and California.

The ongoing loss will not be replaced by evolution in any period of time that has meaning for humanity. Extinction is now proceeding thousands of times faster than the production of new species. The average life span of a species and its descendants in past geological eras varied according to group (like mollusks or echinoderms or flowering plants) from about 1 million to 10 million years. During the past 500 million years, there have been five great extinction spasms comparable to the one now being inaugurated by human expansion. The latest, evidently caused by the collision with Earth of an asteroid, ended the age of reptiles 66 million years ago. In each case it took more than 10 million years of evolution to completely replenish the biodiversity lost. And that was in an otherwise undisturbed natural environment. Humanity is now destroying most of the habitats where evolution can occur.

The surviving biosphere remains the great unknown of Earth in many respects. On the practical side, it is hard even to imagine what other species have to offer in the way of new pharmaceuticals, crops, fibers, petroleum substitutes, and other products. We have only a poor grasp of the ecosystem services by which other organisms cleanse the water, turn soil into a fertile living cover, and manufacture the very air we breathe. We sense but do not fully understand what the highly diverse natural world means to our aesthetic pleasure and mental well-being.

Scientists are unprepared to manage a declining biosphere. To illustrate, consider the following mission they might be given. The last remnant of a rain forest is about to be cut over. Environmentalists are stymied. The contracts have been signed, and local landowners and politicians are intransigent. In a final desperate move, a team of biologists is scrambled in an attempt to preserve the biodiversity by extraordinary means. Their assignment is the following: collect samples of all the species of organisms quickly, before the cutting starts; maintain the species in zoos, gardens, and laboratory cultures or else deep-freeze samples of the tissues in liquid nitrogen; and finally, establish the procedure by which the entire community can be reassembled on empty ground at a later date, when social and economic conditions have improved.

The biologists cannot accomplish this task, not if thousands of them came with a billion-dollar budget. They cannot even imagine how to do it. In the forest patch live legions of species: perhaps 300 birds, 500 butterflies, 200 ants, 50,000 beetles, 1,000 trees, 5,000 fungi, tens of thousands of bacteria, and so on down a long roster of major groups. Each species occupies a precise niche, demanding a certain place, an exact microclimate, particular nutrients and temperature and humidity cycles with specified timing to trigger phases of the life cycle. Many, perhaps most, of the species are locked in symbioses with other species; they cannot survive and reproduce unless arrayed with their partners in the correct idiosyncratic configurations.

Even if the biologists pulled off the taxonomic equivalent of the Manhattan Project in reverse, sorting and preserving cultures of all the species, they could not then put the community back together again. It would be like unscrambling an egg with a pair of spoons. The biology of the microorganisms needed to reanimate the soil would be mostly unknown. The pollinators of most of the flowers and the correct timing of their appearance could only be guessed. The 'assembly rules,' the sequence in which species must be allowed to colonize in order to coexist indefinitely, would remain in the realm of theory.

In its neglect of the rest of life, exemptionalism fails definitively. To move ahead as though scientific and entrepreneurial genius will solve each crisis that arises implies that the declining biosphere can be similarly manipulated. But the world is too complicated to be turned into a garden. There is no biological homeostat that can be worked by humanity; to believe otherwise is to risk reducing a large part of Earth to a wasteland.

The environmentalist vision, prudential and less exuberant than exemptionalism, is closer to reality. It sees humanity entering a bottleneck unique in history, constricted by population and economic pressures. In order to pass through to the other side, within perhaps 50 to 100 years, more science and entrepreneurship will have to be devoted to stabilizing the global environment. That can be accomplished, according to expert consensus, only by halting population growth and devising a wiser use of resources than has been accomplished to date. And wise use for the living world in particular means preserving the surviving ecosystems, micromanaging them only enough to save the biodiversity they contain, until such time as they can be understood and employed in the fullest sense for human benefit.

The Environmental Ethic

The sixth great extinction spasm of geological time is upon us, grace of mankind. Earth has at last acquired a force that can break the crucible of biodiversity. I sensed it with special poignancy that stormy night at Fazenda Dimona*, when lightning flashes revealed the rain forest cut open like a cat's eye for laboratory investigation. An undisturbed forest rarely discloses its internal anatomy with such clarity. Its edge is shielded by thick secondary growth or else, along the river bank, the canopy spills down to ground level. The night-time

* A camp I shared with Brazilian forest workers in the Amazon basin.

vision was a dying artifact, a last glimpse of savage beauty.

A few days later I got ready to leave Fazenda Dimona: gathered my muddied clothes in a bundle, gave my imitation Swiss army knife to the cook as a farewell gift, watched an overflight of Amazonian green parrots one more time, labeled and stored my specimen vials in reinforced boxes, and packed my field notebook next to a dog-eared copy of Ed McBain's police novel *Ice*, which, because I had neglected to bring any other reading matter, was now burned into my memory.

Grinding gears announced the approach of the truck sent to take me and two of the forest workers back to Manaus. In bright sunlight we watched it cross the pastureland, a terrain strewn with fire-blackened stumps and logs, the battlefield my forest had finally lost. On the ride back I tried not to look at the bare fields. Then, abandoning my tourist Portuguese, I turned inward and daydreamed. Four splendid lines of Virgil came to mind, the only ones I ever memorized, where the Sibyl warns Aeneas of the Underworld:

The way downward is easy from Avernus.
Black Dis's door stands open night and day.
But to retrace your steps to heaven's air,
There is the trouble, there is the toil . . .

For the green prehuman earth is the mystery we were chosen to solve, a guide to the birthplace of our spirit, but it is slipping away. The way back seems harder every year. If there is danger in the human trajectory, it is not so much in the survival of our own species as in the fulfillment of the ultimate irony of organic evolution: that in the instant of achieving self-understanding through the mind of man, life has doomed its most beautiful creations. And thus humanity closes the door to its past.

The creation of that diversity came slow and hard: 3 billion years of evolution to start the profusion of animals that occupy the seas, another 350 million years to assemble the rain forests in which half or more of the species on earth now live. There was a succession of dynasties. Some species split into two or several daughter species, and their daughters split yet again to create swarms of descendants that deployed as plant feeders, carnivores, free swimmers, gliders, sprinters, and burrowers, in countless motley combinations. These ensembles then gave way by partial or total extinction to newer dynasties, and so on to form a gentle upward swell that carried biodiversity to a peak – just before the arrival of humans. Life had stalled on plateaus along the way, and on five occasions it suffered extinction spasms that took 10 million years to repair. But the thrust was upward. Today the diversity of life is greater than it was a 100 million years ago – and far greater than 500 million years before that.

Most dynasties contained a few species that expanded disproportionately to create satrapies of lesser rank. Each species and its descendants, a sliver of the whole, lived an average of hundreds of thousands to millions of years. Longevity varied according to taxonomic group. Echinoderm lineages, for example, persisted longer than those of flowering plants, and both endured longer than those of mammals.

Ninety-nine percent of all the species that ever lived are now extinct. The modern fauna

and flora are composed of survivors that some-
how managed to dodge and weave through all
the radiations and extinctions of geological
history. Many contemporary world-dominant
groups, such as rats, ranid frogs, nymphalid
butterflies, and plants of the aster family Com-
positae, attained their status not long before the
Age of Man. Young or old, all living species are
direct descendants of the organisms that lived
3.8 billion years ago. They are living genetic
libraries, composed of nucleotide sequences, the
equivalent of words and sentences, which record
evolutionary events all across that immense
span of time. Organisms more complex than
bacteria – protists, fungi, plants, animals –
contain between 1 and 10 billion nucleotide
letters, more than enough in pure information
to compose an equivalent of the *Encyclopaedia
Britannica*. Each species is the product of muta-
tions and recombinations too complex to be
grasped by unaided intuition. It was sculpted
and burnished by an astronomical number of
events in natural selection, which killed off or
otherwise blocked from reproduction the vast

majority of its member organisms before they completed their lifespans. Viewed from the perspective of evolutionary time, all other species are our distant kin because we share a remote ancestry. We still use a common vocabulary, the nucleic-acid code, even though it has been sorted into radically different hereditary languages.

Such is the ultimate and cryptic truth of every kind of organism, large and small, every bug and weed. The flower in the crannied wall – it is a miracle. If not in the way Tennyson, the Victorian romantic, bespoke the portent of full knowledge (by which 'I should know what God and man is'), then certainly a consequence of all we understand from modern biology. Every kind of organism has reached this moment in time by threading one needle after another, throwing up brilliant artifices to survive and reproduce against nearly impossible odds.

Organisms are all the more remarkable in combination. Pull out the flower from its crannied retreat, shake the soil from the roots into the cupped hand, magnify it for close examination. The black earth is alive with a

riot of algae, fungi, nematodes, mites, spring-
tails, enchytraeid worms, thousands of species
of bacteria. The handful may be only a tiny
fragment of one ecosystem, but because of the
genetic codes of its residents it holds more
order than can be found on the surfaces of all
the planets combined. It is a sample of the
living force that runs the earth – and will continue to do so with or without us.

We may think that the world has been completely explored. Almost all the mountains and
rivers, it is true, have been named, the coast and
geodetic surveys completed, the ocean floor
mapped to the deepest trenches, the atmosphere transected and chemically analyzed. The
planet is now continuously monitored from
space by satellites; and, not least, Antarctica, the
last virgin continent, has become a research station and expensive tourist stop. The biosphere,
however, remains obscure. Even though some
1.4 million species of organisms have been discovered (in the minimal sense of having
specimens collected and formal scientific names
attached), the total number alive on earth is

somewhere between 10 and 100 million. No one can say with confidence which of these figures is the closer. Of the species given scientific names, fewer than 10 percent have been studied at a level deeper than gross anatomy. The revolution in molecular biology and medicine was achieved with a still smaller fraction, including colon bacteria, corn, fruit flies, Norway rats, rhesus monkeys, and human beings, altogether comprising no more than a hundred species.

Enchanted by the continuous emergence of new technologies and supported by generous funding for medical research, biologists have probed deeply along a narrow sector of the front. Now it is time to expand laterally, to get on with the great Linnean enterprise and finish mapping the biosphere. The most compelling reason for the broadening of goals is that, unlike the rest of science, the study of biodiversity has a time limit. Species are disappearing at an accelerating rate through human action, primarily habitat destruction but also pollution and the introduction of exotic species into residual natural environments. I have said that a fifth or more of the species of plants and animals could vanish or be doomed to early extinction by the year 2020 unless better efforts are made to save them. This estimate comes from the known quantitative relation between the area of habitats and the diversity that habitats can sustain. These area-biodiversity curves are supported by the general but not universal principle that when certain groups of organisms are studied closely, such as snails and fishes and flowering plants, extinction is determined to be widespread. And the corollary: among plant and animal remains in archaeological deposits, we usually find extinct species and races. As the last forests are felled in forest strongholds like the Philippines and Ecuador, the decline of species will accelerate even more. In the world as a whole, extinction rates are already hundreds or thousands of times higher than before the coming of man. They cannot be balanced by new evolution in any period of time that has meaning for the human race.

Why should we care? What difference does it make if some species are extinguished, if even half of all the species on earth disappear? Let me count the ways. New sources of scientific information will be lost. Vast potential biological wealth will be destroyed. Still undeveloped medicines, crops, pharmaceuticals, timber, fibers, pulp, soil-restoring vegetation, petroleum substitutes, and other products and amenities will never come to light. It is fashionable in some quarters to wave aside the small and obscure, the bugs and weeds, forgetting that an obscure moth from Latin America saved Australia's pastureland from overgrowth by cactus, that the rosy periwinkle provided the cure for Hodgkin's disease and childhood lymphocytic leukemia, that the bark of the Pacific yew offers hope for victims of ovarian and breast cancer, that a chemical from the saliva of leeches dissolves blood clots during surgery, and so on down a roster already grown long and illustrious despite the limited research addressed to it.

In amnesiac revery it is also easy to overlook the services that ecosystems provide humanity. They enrich the soil and create the very air we breathe. Without these amenities, the remaining tenure of the human race would be nasty and brief. The life-sustaining matrix is built of green plants with legions of microorganisms and mostly small, obscure animals – in other words, weeds and bugs. Such organisms support the world with efficiency because they are so diverse, allowing them to divide labor and swarm over every square meter of the earth's surface. They run the world precisely as we would wish it to be run, because humanity evolved within living communities and our bodily functions are finely adjusted to the idiosyncratic environment already created. Mother Earth is no more than the commonality of organisms and the physical environment they maintain with each passing moment, an environment that will destabilize and turn lethal if the organisms are disturbed too much. A near infinity of other mother planets can be envisioned, each with its own fauna and flora, all producing physical environments uncongenial to human life. To disregard the diversity of life is to risk catapulting ourselves into an alien environment. We will have become like the pilot whales that inexplicably beach themselves on New England shores.

Humanity coevolved with the rest of life on this particular planet; other worlds are not in our genes. Because scientists have yet to put names on most kinds of organisms, and because they entertain only a vague idea of how ecosystems work, it is reckless to suppose that biodiversity can be diminished indefinitely without threatening humanity itself. Field studies show that as biodiversity is reduced, so is the quality of the services provided by ecosystems. Records of stressed ecosystems also demonstrate that the descent can be unpredictably abrupt. As extinction spreads, some of the lost forms prove to be keystone species, whose disappearance brings down other species and triggers a ripple effect through the demographies of the survivors. The loss of a keystone species is like a drill accidentally striking a powerline. It causes lights to go out all over.

These services are important to human welfare. But they cannot form the whole foundation of an enduring environmental ethic. If a price can be put on something, that something can be devalued, sold, and discarded. It is also possible for some to dream that people will go on living comfortably in a biologically impoverished world. They suppose that a prosthetic environment is within the power of technology, that human life can still flourish in a completely humanized world, where medicines would all be synthesized from chemicals off the shelf, food grown from a few dozen domestic crop species, the atmosphere and climate regulated by computer-driven fusion energy, and the earth made over until it becomes a literal spaceship rather than a metaphorical one, with people reading displays and touching buttons on the bridge. Such is the terminus of the philosophy of exemptionalism: do not weep for the past, humanity is a new order of life, let species die if they block progress, scientific and technological genius will find another way. Look up and see the stars awaiting us.

But consider: human advance is determined not by reason alone but by emotions peculiar to our species, aided and tempered by reason.

What makes us people and not computers is emotion. We have little grasp of our true nature, of what it is to be human and therefore where our descendants might someday wish we had directed Spaceship Earth. Our troubles, as Vercors said in *You Shall know Them*, arise from the fact that we do not know what we are and cannot agree on what we want to be. The primary cause of this intellectual failure is ignorance of our origins. We did not arrive on this planet as aliens. Humanity is part of nature, a species that evolved among other species. The more closely we identify ourselves with the rest of life, the more quickly we will be able to discover the sources of human sensibility and acquire the knowledge on which an enduring ethic, a sense of preferred direction, can be built.

The human heritage does not go back only for the conventionally recognized 8,000 years or so of recorded history, but for at least 2 million years, to the appearance of the first 'true' human beings, the earliest species composing the genus *Homo*. Across thousands of generations, the emergence of culture must have been profoundly influenced by simultaneous events in genetic evolution, especially those occurring in the anatomy and physiology of the brain. Conversely, genetic evolution must have been guided forcefully by the kinds of selection rising within culture.

Only in the last moment of human history has the delusion arisen that people can flourish apart from the rest of the living world. Preliterate societies were in intimate contact with a bewildering array of life forms. Their minds could only partly adapt to that challenge. But they struggled to understand the most relevant parts, aware that the right responses gave life and fulfillment, the wrong ones sickness, hunger, and death. The imprint of that effort cannot have been erased in a few generations of urban existence. I suggest that it is to be found among the particularities of human nature, among which are these:

- People acquire phobias, abrupt and intractable aversions, to the objects and circumstances that threaten humanity in natural environments: heights, closed

spaces, open spaces, running water, wolves,
spiders, snakes. They rarely form phobias to
the recently invented contrivances that are
far more dangerous, such as guns, knives,
automobiles, and electric sockets.

• People are both repelled and fascinated by
snakes, even when they have never seen
one in nature. In most cultures the serpent
is the dominant wild animal of mythical
and religious symbolism. Manhattanites
dream of them with the same frequency as
Zulus. This response appears to be
Darwinian in origin. Poisonous snakes
have been an important cause of mortality
almost everywhere, from Finland to
Tasmania, Canada to Patagonia; an
untutored alertness in their presence saves
lives. We note a kindred response in many
primates, including Old World monkeys
and chimpanzees: the animals pull back,
alert others, watch closely, and follow each
potentially dangerous snake until it moves
away. For human beings, in a larger
metaphorical sense, the mythic,

transformed serpent has come to possess
both constructive and destructive powers:
Ashtoreth of the Canaanites, the demons
Fu-Hsi and Nu-kua of the Han Chinese,
Mudamma and Manasa of Hindu India, the
triple-headed giant Nehebkau of the ancient
Egyptians, the serpent of Genesis
conferring knowledge and death, and,
among the Aztecs, Cihuacoatl, goddess of
childbirth and mother of the human race,
the rain god Tlaloc, and Quetzalcoatl, the
plumed serpent with a human head who
reigned as lord of the morning and evening
star. Ophidian power spills over into
modern life: two serpents entwine the
caduceus, first the winged staff of Mercury
as messenger of the gods, then the safe-
conduct pass of ambassadors and heralds,
and today the universal emblem of the
medical profession.

- The favored living place of most peoples is a
  prominence near water from which parkland
  can be viewed. On such heights are found
  the abodes of the powerful and rich, tombs

of the great, temples, parliaments, and monuments commemorating tribal glory. The location is today an aesthetic choice and, by the implied freedom to settle there, a symbol of status. In ancient, more practical times the topography provided a place to retreat and a sweeping prospect from which to spot the distant approach of storms and enemy forces. Every animal species selects a habitat in which its members gain a favorable mix of security and food. For most of deep history, human beings lived in tropical and subtropical savanna in East Africa, open country sprinkled with streams and lakes, trees and copses. In similar topography modern peoples choose their residences and design their parks and gardens, if given a free choice. They simulate neither dense jungles, toward which gibbons are drawn, nor dry grasslands, preferred by hamadryas baboons. In their gardens they plant trees that resemble the acacias, sterculias, and other native trees of the African savannas. The ideal tree crown

sought is consistently wider than tall, with
spreading lowermost branches close enough
to the ground to touch and climb,
clothed with compound or needle-shaped
leaves.

- Given the means and sufficient leisure, a
large portion of the populace backpacks,
hunts, fishes, birdwatches, and gardens. In
the United States and Canada more people
visit zoos and aquariums than attend all
professional athletic events combined. They
crowd the national parks to view natural
landscapes, looking from the tops of
prominences out across rugged terrain for a
glimpse of tumbling water and animals
living free. They travel long distances to
stroll along the seashore, for reasons they
can't put into words.

These are examples of what I have called
biophilia, the connections that human beings
subconsciously seek with the rest of life. To biophilia can be added the idea of wilderness, all
the land and communities of plants and animals

still unsullied by human occupation. Into wilderness people travel in search of new life and wonder, and from wilderness they return to the parts of the earth that have been humanized and made physically secure. Wilderness settles peace on the soul because it needs no help; it is beyond human contrivance. Wilderness is a metaphor of unlimited opportunity, rising from the tribal memory of a time when humanity spread across the world, valley to valley, island to island, godstruck, firm in the belief that virgin land went on forever past the horizon.

I cite these common preferences of mind not as proof of an innate human nature but rather to suggest that we think more carefully and turn philosophy to the central questions of human origins in the wild environment. We do not understand ourselves yet and descend farther from heaven's air if we forget how much the natural world means to us. Signals abound that the loss of life's diversity endangers not just the body but the spirit. If that much is true, the changes occurring now will visit harm on all generations to come.

The ethical imperative should therefore be, first of all, prudence. We should judge every scrap of biodiversity as priceless while we learn to use it and come to understand what it means to humanity. We should not knowingly allow any species or race to go extinct. And let us go beyond mere salvage to begin the restoration of natural environments, in order to enlarge wild populations and stanch the hemorrhaging of biological wealth. There can be no purpose more enspiriting than to begin the age of restoration, reweaving the wondrous diversity of life that still surrounds us.

The evidence of swift environmental change calls for an ethic uncoupled from other systems of belief. Those committed by religion to believe that life was put on earth in one divine stroke will recognize that we are destroying the Creation, and those who perceive biodiversity to be the product of blind evolution will agree. Across the other great philosophical divide, it does not matter whether species have independent rights or, conversely, that moral reasoning is uniquely a human concern. Defenders of both premises seem destined to gravitate toward the same position on conservation.

The stewardship of environment is a domain on the near side of metaphysics where all reflective persons can surely find common ground. For what, in the final analysis, is morality but the command of conscience seasoned by a rational examination of consequences? And what is a fundamental precept but one that serves all generations? An enduring environmental ethic will aim to preserve not only the health and freedom of our species, but access to the world in which the human spirit was born.

Biophilia and the Environmental Ethic

Biophilia, if it exists, and I believe it exists, is the innately emotional affiliation of human beings to other living organisms. From the scant evidence concerning its nature, biophilia is not a single instinct but a complex of learning rules that can be teased apart and analyzed individually. The feelings molded by the learning rules fall along several emotional spectra, from attraction to aversion, awe to indifference, and peacefulness to fear-driven anxiety. These multiple strands of emotional response are woven into symbols composing a large part of culture. When human beings remove themselves from the natural environment, the biophilic learning rules are not replaced by modern versions equally well adapted to contemporary technological features of life. Instead, they persist from generation to generation, atrophied and fitfully manifested in the artificial new environments. It is no accident of culture that more children and adults visit zoos than attend all major professional sports combined (at least in the United States and Canada), that the wealthy continue to seek dwellings on prominences above water amidst parkland, and that urban dwellers continue to dream of snakes for reasons they cannot explain.

Were there no evidence of biophilia at all, the hypothesis of its existence would still be compelled by pure evolutionary logic. The reason is that human history did not begin a mere 8,000 or 10,000 years ago, with the invention of agriculture and villages. It began hundreds of thousands or millions of years ago, with the origin of the genus *Homo*. For more than 99 percent of human history people have lived in hunter-gatherer bands intimately involved with other organisms. During this period of deep history, and still farther back, into paleohominid times, they depended on an exact learned knowledge of crucial aspects of natural history. That much is true even of chimpanzees today, who use primitive tools and have a practical knowledge of plants and animals. As language and culture expanded, humans also used living organisms of diverse kinds as a principal source of metaphor and myth. In short, the brain evolved in a biocentric world, not a machine-regulated one. It would therefore be quite extraordinary to find that all learning rules related to that world had been erased in a few thousand years, even in the tiny minority of humans who have existed for more than one or two generations in wholly urban environments.

The significance of biophilia in human biology is potentially profound, even if it exists solely as weak learning rules. It is relevant to our thinking about nature, about the landscape, the arts, and mythopoeia, and it invites us to take a new look at environmental ethics.

How could biophilia have evolved? The likely answer is biocultural evolution, during which culture was elaborated under the influence of hereditary learning propensities while the genes prescribing the propensities were spread by natural selection in a cultural context. The learning rules can be inaugurated and fine-tuned variously by an adjustment of sensory thresholds, by a quickening or blockage of learning, and by modification of emotional responses. Charles Lumsden and I have envisioned biocultural evolution to be of a particular kind, gene-culture coevolution, which traces a spiral trajectory through time: a certain genotype makes a behavioral response more likely, the response enhances survival and reproductive fitness, the genotype consequently spreads through the population, and the behavioral response grows more frequent. Add to this the strong general tendency of human beings to translate emotions into myriad dreams and narratives, and the necessary conditions are in place to cut the historical channels of art and religious belief.

Gene-culture coevolution is a plausible explanation for the origin of biophilia. The hypothesis can be made explicit by the human relation to snakes. The sequence I envision is the following, drawn principally from elements established by the art historian and biologist Balaji Mundkur:

- Poisonous snakes cause sickness and death in primates and other mammals throughout the world.
- Old World monkeys and apes generally combine a strong natural fear of snakes with fascination for these animals and the use of vocal communication, the latter including specialized sounds in a few species, all drawing attention of the group to the presence of snakes in the near vicinity. Thus alerted, the group follows the intruders until they leave.
- Human beings are also genetically averse to snakes. They are quick to develop fear and even full-blown phobias with very little negative reinforcement. (Other phobic elements in the natural environment include dogs, spiders, closed spaces, running water, and heights. Few if any modern artifacts are as effective, including even those most dangerous,

such as guns, knives, automobiles, and electric wires.)

• In a manner true to their status as Old World primates, human beings are also fascinated by snakes. They pay admission to see captive specimens in zoos. They employ snakes profusely as metaphors and weave them into stories, myth, and religious symbolism. The serpent gods of cultures they have conceived all around the world are furthermore typically ambivalent. Often semihuman in form, they are poised to inflict vengeful death but also to bestow knowledge and power.

• People in diverse cultures dream more about serpents than about any other kind of animal, conjuring as they do so a rich medley of dread and magical power. When shamans and religious prophets report such images, they invest them with mystery and symbolic authority. In what seems to be a logical consequence, serpents are also prominent agents in mythology and religion in a majority of cultures.

Here then is the ophidian version of biophilia hypothesis expressed in briefest form: constant exposure through evolutionary time to the malign influence of snakes, the repeated experience encoded by natural selection as a hereditary aversion and fascination, which in turn is manifested in the dreams and stories of evolving cultures. I would expect that other biophilic responses have originated more or less independently, by the same means but under different selection pressures and with the involvement of different gene ensembles and brain circuitry.

Of course, this formulation is fair enough as a working hypothesis, but we must also ask how such elements can be distinguished, and how the general biophilia hypothesis might be tested. One mode of analysis, reported by Jared Diamond, is the correlative analysis of knowledge and attitude of peoples in diverse cultures, designed to search for common denominators in the total human pattern of response. Another, advanced by Robert Ulrich and other psychologists, is the precisely replicated measurement of the physiological responses of human subjects to both attractive and aversive natural phenomena. This direct psychological approach can be made increasingly persuasive, whether for or against a biological bias, when two elements are added. The first is the measurement of heritability in the intensity of the responses to the psychological tests used. The second element is the tracing of cognitive development in children to identify key stimuli that evoke the responses, along with the ages of maximum sensitivity and learning propensity. For example, the slithering motion of an elongate form appears to be the key stimulus producing snake aversion, and preadolescence may be the maximally sensitive period for acquiring the aversion.

Given that humanity's relation to the natural environment is as much a part of deep history as social behavior itself, cognitive psychologists have been strangely slow to address its mental consequences. Our ignorance could be regarded as just one more blank space on the map of academic science, awaiting genius and initiative, except for one important circumstance: the natural environment is disappearing. As a consequence, psychologists and other scholars are obligated to consider biophilia in more urgent terms. What, they should ask, will happen to the human psyche when such a defining part of the human evolutionary experience is diminished or erased?

There is no question in my mind that the most harmful part of ongoing environmental despoliation is the loss of biodiversity. The reason is that the variety of organisms, from alleles (differing gene forms) to species, once lost, cannot be regained. If diversity is sustained in wild ecosystems, the biosphere can be recovered and used by future generations to any degree desired and with benefits literally beyond measure. To the extent it is diminished, humanity will be poorer for all generations to come. How much poorer? The following estimates give a rough idea:

- Consider first the question of the amount of biodiversity. The number of species of organisms on Earth is unknown to the nearest order of magnitude. About 1.5 million species have been given names to date, but the actual number is likely to lie somewhere between 10 and 100 million. Among the least-known groups are the fungi, with 69,000 known species but 1.6 million thought to exist. Also poorly explored are at least several million and possibly tens of millions of species of arthropods in the tropical rain forests; and millions of invertebrate species on the vast floor of the deep sea. The true black hole of systematics, however, may be bacteria. Although roughly 4,000 species have been formally described, recent studies in Norway have indicated the presence of from 4,000 to 5,000 species, almost all new to science, among the 10 billion individual organisms found on average in each gram of forest soil, and another 4,000 to 5,000 species, different from the first set and also mostly new, in an average gram of nearby marine sediments.

- Fossil records of marine invertebrates, African ungulates, and flowering plants indicate that under natural conditions each clade – a species and its descendants – lasts an average of 500,000 to 10 million years. The longevity is measured from the time the ancestral form splits off from its sister species to the time of the extinction of the last descendant. It varies according to the group of organisms. Mammals, for example, are shorter-lived than invertebrates.
- Bacteria contain on the order of a million nucleotide pairs in their genetic code, and more complex (eukaryotic) organisms from algae to flowering plants and mammals contain one to 10 billion nucleotide pairs.
- Because of their great age and genetic complexity, species are exquisitely adapted to the ecosystems in which they live.
- The number of species on Earth is being reduced by a rate from 100 to 1,000 times higher than in prehuman times. The current removal rate of tropical rain forest, over 1 percent of cover each

year, translates (if we use the most conservative parameter value) to approximately 0.3 percent of the species extirpated immediately or at least doomed to much earlier extinction than would otherwise have been the case. Most systematists with global expressions believe that more than half the species of organisms on earth live in the tropical rain forests. If there are 10 million species in these habitats – a conservative estimate – the rate of loss may be 30,000 a year, 74 a day, 3 an hour. This rate, though horrendous, is actually a minimal estimate, in the sense that it is based on the area-species relation alone. It does not take into account extinction due to pollution, disturbance short of clear-cutting, and the introduction of exotic species.

Other species-rich habitats, including coral reefs, river systems, lakes, and Mediterranean-type heathland, are under similar assault. When the final remnants of such habitats are destroyed

in a region – the last of the ridges on a moun-
tainside cleared, for example, or the last riffles
flooded by a downstream dam – species are
wiped out en masse. The first 90 percent reduction in area of a habitat lowers the species
number by one-half. The final 10 percent elimi-
nates the second half.

It is a guess, subjective but very defensible,
that if the current rate of habitat alteration continues unchecked, 20 percent or more of the
Earth's species will disappear or be consigned to
early extinction through human action taken
during the next thirty years. From prehistory to
the present time humanity has probably already
eliminated 10 or even 20 percent of the species.
The number of bird species, for example, is
down by an estimated 25 percent, from 12,000 to
9,000, with a disproportionate share of the losses
occurring on islands. Most of the megafaunas –
the largest mammals and birds – appear to have
been destroyed in more remote parts of the
world by the first wave of hunter-gatherers and
agriculturists millennia ago. The loss of plants
and invertebrates is likely to have been much

smaller, but studies of archaeological and other subfossil deposits are too few to permit even a crude estimate. The human impact, from prehistory to the present time and projected into the next several decades, threatens to be the greatest extinction spasm since the end of the Mesozoic era, 65 million years ago.

Assume, for the sake of argument, that 10 percent of the world's species that existed just before the advent of humanity are already gone, and that another 20 percent are destined to vanish quickly unless drastic action is taken. The fraction lost – and it will be a great deal no matter what action is taken – cannot be replaced by evolution in any period that has meaning for the human mind. Following each of the five previous major spasms of the past 550 million years, life required about 10 million years of natural evolution to recover. What humanity is doing now in a single lifetime will impoverish our descendants for virtually all time to come. Yet critics often respond, 'So what? If only half the species survive, that is still a lot of biodiversity – is it not?'

The answer most frequently urged right now by conservationists, myself among them, is that the vast material wealth offered by biodiversity is at risk. Wild species are an untapped source of new pharmaceuticals, crops, fibers, pulp, petroleum substitutes, and agents for the restoration of soil and water. This argument is demonstrably true – and it certainly tends to stop anti-conservation libertarians in their tracks – but it contains a dangerous practical flaw when relied upon exclusively. If species are to be judged by their potential material value, they can be priced, traded off against other sources of wealth, and – when the price is right – discarded. Yet who can judge the *ultimate* value of any particular species to humanity? Whether the species offers immediate advantage or not, no means exist to measure what benefits it will offer during future centuries of study, what scientific knowledge, or what service to the human spirit.

At last I have come to the word so hard to express, spirit. With reference to the spirit we arrive at the connection between biophilia and the environmental ethic. The great philosophical divide in moral reasoning about the remainder of life is whether or not other species have an innate right to exist. That decision rests in turn on the most fundamental question of all, whether moral values exist apart from humanity, in the same manner as mathematical laws, or whether they are idiosyncratic constructs that evolved in the human mind through natural selection, and thus of the spirit. Had a species other than humans attained high intelligence and culture, it would probably have fashioned different moral values. Civilized termites, for example, would support cannibalism of the sick and injured, eschew personal reproduction, and make a sacrament of the exchange and consumption of feces. The termite 'spirit,' in short, would have been immensely different from the human spirit, horrifying to us in fact. The constructs of moral reasoning, in this evolutionary view, are the learning rules, the propensities to acquire or to resist certain emotions and kinds of knowledge. They have evolved genetically because they confer survival and reproduction on human beings.

The first of the two alternative propositions – that species have universal and independent rights, regardless of how else human beings feel about the matter – may be true. To the extent the proposition is accepted, it will certainly steel the determination of environmentalists to preserve the remainder of life. But the species-right argument alone, like the materialistic argument alone, is a dangerous gambit on which to risk biodiversity. Its reasoning, for all its directness and power, remains intuitive, aprioristic, and lacking in objective evidence. Who but humanity, it can be immediately asked, gives such rights? Where is the enabling canon written? And such rights, even if granted, are always subject to rank-ordering and relaxation. A simplistic adjuration for the right of a species to live can be answered by a simplistic call for the right of people to live. If a last section of forest needs to be cut to perpetuate the survival of a local economy, the rights of the myriad species in the forest may be cheerfully recognized but given a lower and fatal priority.

Without attempting to resolve the issue of the innate rights of species, I will argue the necessity of a robust and richly textured anthropocentric ethic apart from the issue of rights, one based on the hereditary needs of our own species. In addition to the well-documented utilitarian potential of wild species, the diversity of life has immense aesthetic and spiritual value. The ideas outlined below are already familiar to many conservationists and ethicists, yet the evolutionary logic is still relatively new and poorly explored, and therein lies the challenge to scientists and other scholars.

Biodiversity is the Creation. Ten million or more species are still alive, each defined by up to billions of nucleotide pairs and a far larger, in fact astronomical, number of possible genetic recombinants. These constitute the arena in which evolution continues to occur. Despite the fact that living organisms compose a mere one ten-billionth part of the mass of Earth, biodiversity is the most information-rich part of the known universe. More organization and complexity exist in a handful of soil than on the surfaces of all the other planets combined. If humanity is to have a satisfying creation myth consistent with scientific knowledge – a myth that itself seems to be an essential part of the human spirit – the narrative will find its starting point in the origin of the diversity of life.

Other species are our kin. This perception is literally true in evolutionary time. All higher eukaryotic organisms, from flowering plants to insects and humanity itself, are thought to have descended from a single ancestral population that lived about 1.8 billion years ago. Single-celled eukaryotes and bacteria are linked by still more remote ancestors. This distant kinship is stamped by a common genetic code and elementary features of cell structure. Humanity did not soft-land into the teeming biosphere like an alien from another planet. We arose from other organisms already here, whose great diversity, conducting experiment upon experiment in the production of new life forms, eventually hit upon the human species.

The biodiversity of a country is part of its national heritage. Each country in turn possesses its own unique assemblages of plants and animals, including, in almost all cases, species and geographic races found nowhere else. Those assemblages are the product of the deep history of the national territory, extending back long before the coming of man.

Biodiversity is the frontier of the future. Humanity needs a vision of an expanding and unending future. That spiritual craving cannot be satisfied by the colonization of space. The other planets are inhospitable and immensely expensive to reach. The nearest stars are so far away that voyagers would need thousands of years just to report back. The true frontier for humanity is life on Earth – its exploration and the transport of knowledge about it into science, art, and practical affairs. The circumstances that validate the proposition are, to repeat briefly: 90 percent or more of the species of plants, animals, and microorganisms lack even so much as a scientific name; each of the species is immensely old by human standards and has been wonderfully molded to its environment; life around us exceeds in complexity and beauty anything else humanity is ever likely to encounter.

The manifold ways by which human beings are tied to the remainder of life are very poorly understood, crying for new scientific inquiry and bold aesthetic interpretation. The portmanteau terms 'biophilia' and 'biophilia hypothesis' will serve well if they do no more than call attention to psychological phenomena that rose from deep human history, stemmed from interaction with the natural environment, and are now quite likely resident in the genes themselves. The search is rendered more urgent by the rapid disappearance of the living part of that environment, creating a need not only for a better understanding of human nature but for a more powerful and intellectually convincing environmental ethic based upon it.

Vanishing Before Our Eyes

Known as the biosphere to scientists and as the creation to theologians, all of life together consists of a membrane around earth so thin that it cannot be seen edgewise from a satellite yet so prodigiously diverse that only a tiny fraction of species have been discovered and named. The products of billions of years of evolution, organisms occupy virtually every square centimeter of the planet's surfaces and fill nearly every imaginable niche.

Biologists estimate that more than half the species occur in the tropical rain forests. From these natural greenhouses, many world records of biodiversity have been reported – 425 kinds of trees in 2.5 acres (1 hectare) of Brazil's Atlantic forest and 1,300 butterfly species from a corner of Peru's Manu National Park, both more than 10 times the number from comparable sites in Europe and North America. At the other extreme, the McMurdo Dry Valleys of Antarctica, with the poorest and coldest soils in the world, still harbor sparse communities of bacteria, fungi and microscopic invertebrate animals.

A few remarkable species, the 'extremophiles,' have achieved astonishing feats of physiological adaptation at the ends of habitable Earth. In the most frigid polar waters, fish and other animals flourish, their blood kept fluid by biochemical antifreezes. Populations of bacteria live in the spumes of volcanic thermal vents on the ocean floor, multiplying in water above the boiling point.

And far beneath Earth's surface, to a depth of 2 miles (3.2 km) or more, dwell the slimes (subsurface lithoautotrophic microbial ecosystems), unique assemblages of bacteria and fungi that occupy pores in the interlocking mineral grains of igneous rock and derive their energy from inorganic chemicals. The slimes are independent of the world above, so even if all of it were burned to a cinder, they would carry on and, given enough time, probably evolve new life-forms able to re-enter the world of air and sunlight.

Earth's biodiversity (short for biological diversity) is organized into three levels. At the top are the ecosystems, such as rain forests, coral reefs and lakes. Next down are the species that compose the ecosystems: swallowtail butterflies, moray eels, people. At the bottom are the variety of genes making up the heredity of each species. How much biodiversity is there? Biologists have described a total of between 1.5 million and 1.8 million species. Yet this impressive achievement is only a small beginning. Estimates of the true number of living species range, according to the method employed, from 3.6 million to more than 100 million.

Least known are the smallest organisms. By repeated sampling, biologists estimate that as few as ten percent of the different kinds of insects, nematode worms and fungi have been discovered. For bacteria and other microorganisms, the number could be well below one percent. Even the largest and most intensively studied organisms are incompletely cataloged. Four species of mammals, for example, have recently been discovered in the remote Annamite Mountains along the Vietnam-Laos border. One of them, the saola or spindlehorn, is a large cowlike animal distinct enough to be classified in a genus of its own. Earth, as far as life is concerned, is still a little-known planet.

Biologists who explore biodiversity see it vanishing before their eyes. To use two of their favorite phrases, they live in a world of wounds and practice a scientific discipline with a deadline. They generally agree that the rate of species extinction is now 100 to 1,000 times as great as it was before the coming of humanity. Throughout most of geological time, individual species and their immediate descendants lived an average of about 1 million years. They disappeared naturally at the rate of about one species per million per year, and newly evolved species replaced them at the same rate, maintaining a rough equilibrium. No longer. Not only has the extinction rate soared, but also the birthrate of new species has declined as the natural environment is destroyed. The principal cause of both extinction and the slowing of evolution is the degrading and destruction of habitats by human action. While covering only six percent of Earth's land surface, about the same as the 48 contiguous United States, the rain forests are losing an area about half the size of Florida each year.

Damage to intact forests, which occurs when they are broken up into isolated patches or partly logged, or when fires are set, threatens biodiversity still more. With other rich environments under similar assault, including coral reefs (two-thirds degraded) and salt marshes and mangrove swamps (half eliminated or radically altered), the extinction rate of species and races is everywhere rising.

Not all doomed species disappear immediately. Most first suffer loss of their ranges and gene pool to dangerously low levels, eventually descending to join what biologists call the 'living dead.' Throughout the world, 976 tree species, for example, are classified as critically endangered. Two are down to three or four surviving individuals and three others to only one. I have been grimly compiling what I call the Hundred Heartbeat Club of animal species – those consisting of a hundred or fewer individuals, hence that number of heartbeats away from total extinction. The club's more familiar members include the Javan rhinoceros, Philippine eagle, Hawaiian crow, Spix's macaw and Chinese river dolphin. Other endangered species lined up for early admission are the giant panda, Sumatran rhinoceros and mountain gorilla.

Paleontologists recognize six previous mass-extinction events during the past half-billion years (the number was until recently believed to be five, but now another, from early Cambrian times, has been added). The last and most famous, which occurred 65 million years ago and was caused by a giant meteorite strike off the present-day coast of Yucatán, ended the age of dinosaurs. These catastrophes followed a typical sequence. First, a large part of biodiversity was destroyed. There was a bloom of a small number of 'disaster species,' such as medleys of fungi and ferns, that survived and reproduced rapidly to fill the habitable spaces emptied of other life. As more time passed, a few 'Lazarus species' reappeared in localities from which they had been wiped out, having been able to spread from isolated pockets difficult to detect. Then, very slowly, across 2 million to 5 million or more years, life as a whole evolved again to its full, original variety.

Researchers of biodiversity agree that we are in the midst of the seventh mass extinction. Even if the current rate of habitat destruction were to continue in forests and coral reefs alone, half the species of plants and animals would be gone by the end of the 21st century. Our descendants would inherit a biologically impoverished and homogenized world. Not only would there be many fewer life forms, but also faunas and floras would look much the same over large parts of the world, with disaster species such as fire ants and house mice widely spread. Humanity would then have to wait millions of years for natural evolution to replace what was lost in a single century.

In the long term, I am convinced, the quenching of life's exuberance will be more consequential to humanity than all of present-day global warming, ozone depletion and pollution combined. Why? For practical reasons, if nothing else. Humanity's food supply comes from a dangerously narrow sliver of biodiversity. Throughout history, people have cultivated or gathered 7,000 plant species for food. Today only 20 species provide ninety percent of the world's food and three – maize, wheat and rice – supply more than half. Tens of thousands of species of the world's still surviving flora can be bred or provide genes to increase production in deserts, saline flats and other marginal habitats.

Natural pharmaceuticals offered by biodiversity are also underutilized. Only a few hundred wild species have served to stock our antibiotics, anticancer agents, pain killers and blood thinners. The biochemistry of the vast majority – millions – of other species is an unfathomed reservoir of new and potentially more effective substances. The reason is to be found in the principles of evolutionary biology. Caught in an endless arms race, these species have devised myriad ways to combat microbes and cancer-causing runaway cells.

We have scarcely begun to consult them for the experience stored in their genes.

If the future enhancement of agriculture and medicine is not thought enough to merit conservation, then consider survival. The biosphere gives us renewed soils, energy, clean water and the very air we breathe, all free of charge. The more species that compose wild communities, the more stable and resilient becomes the planet as a whole.

Then consider ethics. More and more leaders of science and religion now pose this question: Who are we to destroy or even diminish biodiversity and thus the creation? Look more closely at nature, they say; every species is a masterpiece, exquisitely adapted to the particular environment in which it has survived for thousands to millions of years. It is part of the world – part of Eden if you prefer – in which our own species arose.

The profligacy of the 20th century has led humanity into a bottleneck of overpopulation and shrinking natural resources. Through this bottleneck humanity and the rest of life must now pass. By the end of the new century, if we are both lucky and wise, we will exit in better shape than we entered, with the population peaked around 8 billion or less and a gradual decline begun.

People everywhere will have acquired a decent quality of life, with the expectation of more improvement to come. One of the defining goals of the century must also be to settle humanity down before we wreck the planet. To that end it is important to accept the challenge and responsibility of global conservation – and to do so right now, before it is too late. We will be judged by the amount of biodiversity we carry through the bottleneck with us. There are reasons to be warily optimistic that biodiversity may be salvageable. Whether it happens in time depends fundamentally on the shift to a new ethic, which sees humanity as part of the biosphere and its faithful steward, not just the resident master and economic maximizer. That change of heart has begun in most countries among a few farsighted leaders and a growing part of the general public, albeit very slowly.

Success also depends on attention to sustainable management of the environment, including protection of biodiversity. Conservation experts now give top priority to 'hot spots,' pockets of wild nature that contain high concentrations of endangered species, which give hope that a great deal can be accomplished in a short span of time. From the coastal sage of California to the rain forests of West Africa, the hottest of the terrestrial hot spots occupy only 1.4 percent of the world's land surface yet are the exclusive home of more than a third of the terrestrial plant and vertebrate species. Similarly, from the streams of Appalachia to the Philippine coral reefs, aquatic hot spots occupy a tiny fraction of the shallow water surface. This much of the world can be set aside quickly without crippling economic or social consequences. More difficult but equally important are the preservation and long-term nondestructive use of the remaining fragments of the old-growth forests, including the tropical wildernesses of Asia, Central Africa and Latin America. None of this will be easy, but no great goal ever was. Surely nothing can be more important than to secure the future of the rest of life and thereby to safeguard our own.

Half-Earth

Unstanched haemorrhaging has only one end in all biological systems: death for an organism, extinction for a species. Researchers who study the trajectory of biodiversity loss are alarmed that, within the century, an exponentially rising extinction rate might easily wipe out most of the species still surviving at the present time.

The crucial factor in the life and death of species is the amount of suitable habitat left to them. When, for example, ninety percent of the area is removed, the number that can persist sustainably will descend to about a half. Such is the actual condition of many of the most species-rich localities around the world, including Madagascar, the Mediterranean perimeter, parts of continental southwestern Asia, Polynesia, and many of the islands of the Philippines and the West Indies. If ten percent of the remaining natural habitat were then also removed – a team of lumbermen might do it in a month – most or all of the surviving resident species would disappear.

Today, every sovereign nation in the world has a protected-area system of some kind. All together the reserves number about 161,000 on land and 6,500 over marine waters. According to the World Database on Protected Areas, a joint project of the United Nations Environmental Program and the International Union for Conservation of Nature, they occupied by 2015 a little less than fifteen percent of Earth's land area and 2.8 per cent of Earth's ocean area. The coverage is increasing gradually. This trend is encouraging. To have reached the existing level is a tribute to those who have led and participated in the global conservation effort.

But is the level enough to halt the acceleration of species extinction? Unfortunately, it is in fact nowhere close to enough. The declining world of biodiversity cannot be saved by the piecemeal operations in current use alone. The extinction rate our behaviour is now imposing on the rest of life, and seems destined to continue, is more correctly viewed as the equivalent of a Chicxulub-sized asteroid strike played out over several human generations.

The only hope for the species still living is a human effort commensurate with the magnitude of the problem. The ongoing mass extinction of species, and with it the extinction of genes and ecosystems, ranks with pandemics, world war, and climate change as among the deadliest threats that humanity has imposed on itself. To those who feel content to let the Anthropocene evolve toward whatever destiny it mindlessly drifts, I say please take time to reconsider. To those who are steering the growth of reserves worldwide, let me make an earnest request: don't stop, just aim a lot higher.

I see just one way to make this 11th-hour save: committing half of the planet's surface to nature to save the immensity of life-forms that compose it. Why one-half? Why not one-quarter or one-third? Because large plots, whether they already stand or can be created from corridors connecting smaller plots, harbour many more ecosystems and the species composing them at a sustainable level. As reserves grow in size, the diversity of life surviving within them also grows. As reserves are reduced in area, the diversity within them declines to a mathematically predictable degree swiftly – often immediately and, for a large fraction, forever. A biogeographic scan of Earth's principal habitats shows that a full representation of its ecosystems and the vast majority of its species can be saved within half the planet's surface. At one-half and above, life on Earth enters the safe zone. Within half, existing calculations from existing ecosystems indicate that more than 80 per cent of the species would be stabilised.

There is a second, psychological argument for protecting half of Earth. The current conservation movement has not been able to go the distance because it is a process. It targets the most endangered habitats and species and works forward from there. Knowing that the conservation window is closing fast, it strives to add increasing amounts of protected space, faster and faster, saving as much as time and opportunity will allow.

Half-Earth is different. It is a goal. People understand and prefer goals. They need a victory, not just news that progress is being made. It is human nature to yearn for finality, something achieved by which their anxieties and fears are put to rest.

The Half-Earth solution does not mean dividing the planet into hemispheric halves or any other large pieces the size of continents or nation-states. Nor does it require changing ownership of any of the pieces, but instead only the stipulation that they be allowed to exist unharmed. It does, on the other hand, mean setting aside the largest reserves possible for nature, hence for the millions of other species still alive.

The key to saving one-half of the planet is the ecological footprint, defined as the amount of space required to meet all of the needs of an average person. It comprises the land used for habitation, fresh water, food production and delivery, personal transportation, communication, governance, other public functions, medical support, burial, and entertainment. In the same way the ecological footprint is scattered in pieces around the world, so are Earth's surviving wildlands on the land and in the sea. The pieces range in size from the major desert and forest wildernesses to pockets of restored habitats as small as a few hectares.

But, you may ask, doesn't a rising population and per-capita consumption doom the Half-Earth prospect? In this aspect of its biology, humanity appears to have won a throw of the demographic dice. Its population growth has begun to decelerate autonomously, without pressure one way or the other from law or custom. In every country where women have gained some degree of social and financial independence, their average fertility has dropped by a corresponding amount through individual personal choice.

There won't be an immediate drop in the total world population. An overshoot still exists due to the longevity of the more numerous offspring of earlier, more fertile generations. There also remain high-fertility countries, with an average of more than three surviving children born to each woman, thus higher than the 2.1 children per woman that yields zero population growth. Even as it decelerates toward zero growth, population will reach between 9.6 billion and 12.3 billion, up from the 7.2 billion existing in 2014. That is a heavy burden for an already overpopulated planet to bear, but unless women worldwide switch back from the negative population trend of fewer than 2.1 children per woman, a turn downward in the early 22nd century is inevitable.

And what of per-capita consumption? The footprint will evolve, not to claim more and more space, as you might at first suppose, but less. The reason lies in the evolution of the free market system, and the way it is increasingly shaped by high technology. The products that win are those that cost less to manufacture and advertise, need less frequent repair and replacement, and give highest performance with a minimum amount of energy. Just as natural selection drives organic evolution by competition among genes to produce more copies of themselves per unit cost in the next generation, raising benefit-to-cost of production drives the evolution of the economy. Teleconferencing, online purchase and trade, ebook personal libraries, access on the Internet to all literature and scientific data, online diagnosis and medical practice, food production per hectare sharply raised by indoor vertical gardens with LED lighting, genetically engineered crops and microorganisms, long-distance business conferences and social visits by life-sized images, and not least the best available education in the world free online to anyone, anytime, and anywhere. All of these amenities will yield more and better results with less per-capita material and energy, and thereby will reduce the size of the ecological footprint.

The spearhead of this intensive economic evolution, with its hope for biodiversity, is contained in the linkage of biology, nanotechnology, and robotics. These three industries have the potential either to favor biodiversity or to destroy it.

I believe they will favor it, by moving the

economy away from fossil fuels to energy sources that are clean and sustainable, by radically improving agriculture with new crop species and ways to grow them, and by reducing the need or even the desire for distant travel. All are primary goals of the digital revolution. Through them the size of the ecological footprint will also be reduced. The average person can expect to enjoy a longer, healthier life of high quality yet with less energy extraction and raw demand put on the land and sea. If we are lucky (and smart), world population will peak at a little more than 10 billion people by the end of the century followed by the ecological footprint soon thereafter. The reason is that we are thinking organisms trying to understand how the world works. We will come awake.

That process is already under way, albeit still far too slowly – with the end in sight in the twenty-third century. We and the rest of life with us are in the middle of a bottleneck of rising population, shrinking resources, and disappearing species. As its stewards we need to think of our species as being in a race to save the living environment. The primary goal is to make it through the bottleneck to a better, less perilous existence while carrying through as much of the rest of life as possible. If global biodiversity is given space and security, most of the large fraction of species now endangered will regain sustainability on their own. Furthermore, advances made in synthetic biology, artificial intelligence, whole brain emulation, and other similar, mathematically based disciplines can be imported to create an authentic, predictive science of ecology. In it, the interrelations of species will be explored as fervently as we now search through our own bodies for health and longevity. It is often said that the human brain is the most complex system known to us in the universe. That is incorrect. The most complex is the individual natural ecosystem, and the collectivity of ecosystems comprising Earth's species-level biodiversity. Each species of plant, animal, fungus, and microorganism is guided by sophisticated decision devices. Each is intricately programmed in its own way to pass with precision through its respective life cycle. It is instructed on when to grow, when to mate, when to disperse, and when to shy away from enemies. Even the single-celled *Escherichia coli*, living in the bacterial paradise of our intestines, moves toward food and away from toxins by spinning its tail cilium one way, then the other way, in response to chemosensory molecules within its microscopic body.

It is past time to broaden the discussion of the human future and connect it to the rest of life. The Silicon Valley dreamers of a digitized humanity have not done that, not yet. They have failed to give much thought at all to the biosphere. With the human condition changing so swiftly, we are losing or degrading to uselessness ever more quickly the millions of species that have run the world independently of us and free of cost. If humanity continues its suicidal ways to change the global climate, eliminate ecosystems, and exhaust Earth's natural resources, our species will very soon find itself forced into making a choice, this time engaging the conscious part of our brain. It is as follows: shall we be existential conservatives, keeping our genetically-based human nature while tapering off the activities inimical to ourselves and the rest of the biosphere? Or shall we use our new technology to accommodate the changes important solely to our own species, while letting the rest of life slip away? We have only a short time to decide.

The beautiful world our species inherited took the biosphere 3.8 billion years to build. The intricacy of its species we know only in part, and the way they work together to create a sustainable balance we have only recently begun to grasp. Like it or not, and prepared or not, we are the mind and stewards of the living world. Our own ultimate future depends upon that understanding. We have come a very long way through the barbaric period in which we still live, and now I believe we've learned enough to adopt a transcendent moral precept concerning the rest of life.